W9-DES-369

AN·IMAGICATION·BOOK


Library of Congress Catalog Card Number: 62-7496


# LET'S IMAGINE SOUNDS

WORDS by
JANET WOLFF
PICTURES by
BERNARD OWETT

E.P. DUTTON COMPANY INC.
NEW YORK

Sometimes when the house is quiet . . .

and your baby sister or brother is sleeping . . .

and everyone says –
SSSHHH!

It's a good time to imagine noises
instead of
making them.

This is a game that's fun to play. You just think of a sound and imagine all the things that sound can be. NOW LET'S PLAY. . . .

Now let's imagine a sound like

**BANG!**

Bang is a loud sound. . . .

It is a sound that startles you.

BANG
can be a falling suitcase.
BANG
can be a rifle
shooting.
BANG
can be a door
slamming!
What else do you imagine
a sound like BANG can be?

# Did you imagine any of these?

A balloon bursting

A hammer hitting a nail

Pounding on a piano

A bat hitting a baseball

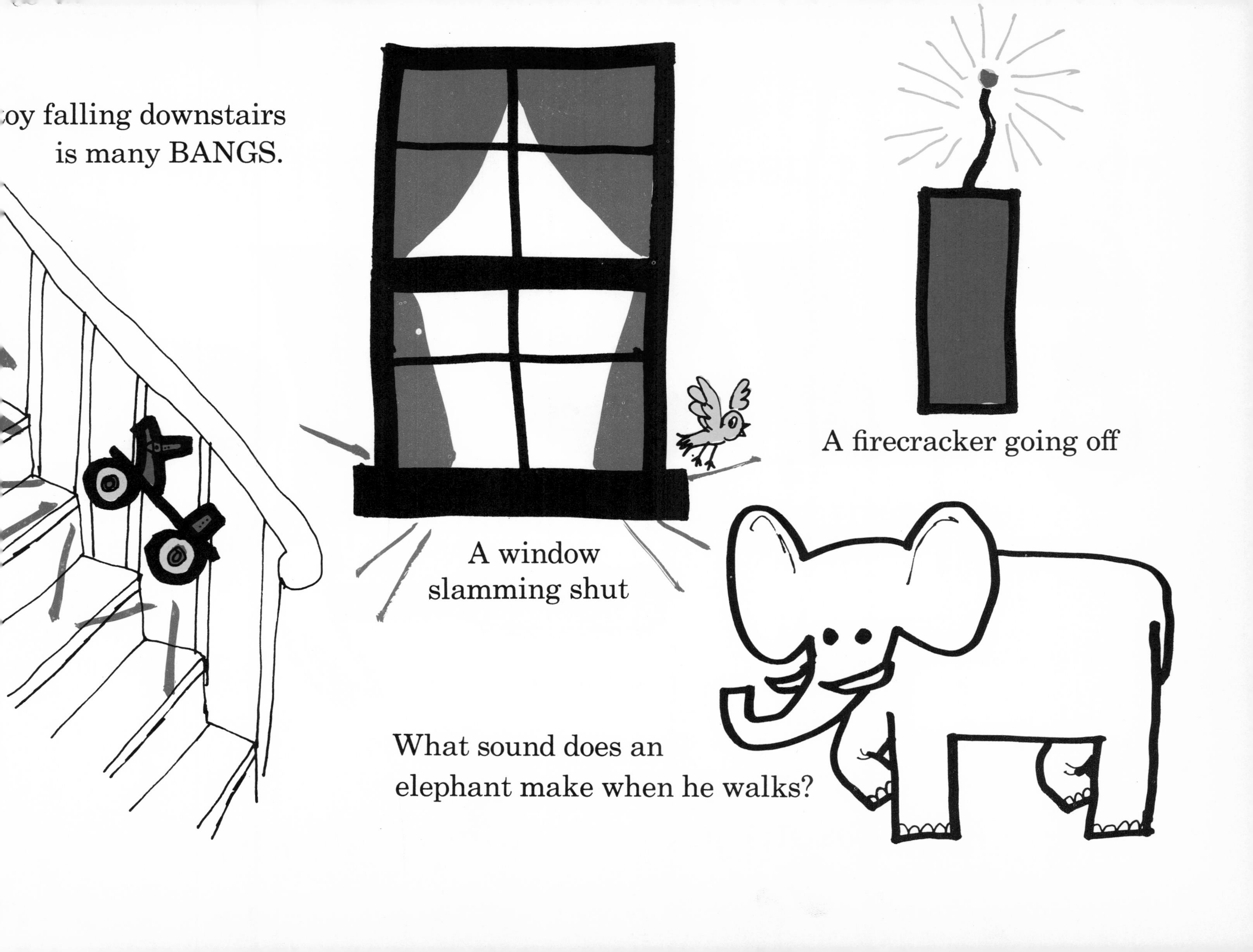
oy falling downstairs
is many BANGS.
A window
slamming shut
A firecracker going off
What sound does an
elephant make when he walks?

Now let's imagine a sound like

PLOP!

p is a soft, lazy sound. It doesn't startle you.

**PLOP**
is the sound of your slipper
dropping to the floor.

**PLOP**
can be a pebble
falling into water.

**PLOP**
can be a ball
caught in
a glove.

What other
things can
a sound
like PLOP be?

# Did you imagine any of these?

A flat tire going round and round

Dumpling dropped into soup

A belly flop
in a pool

Soap falling into a bathtub

Raindrops on a window

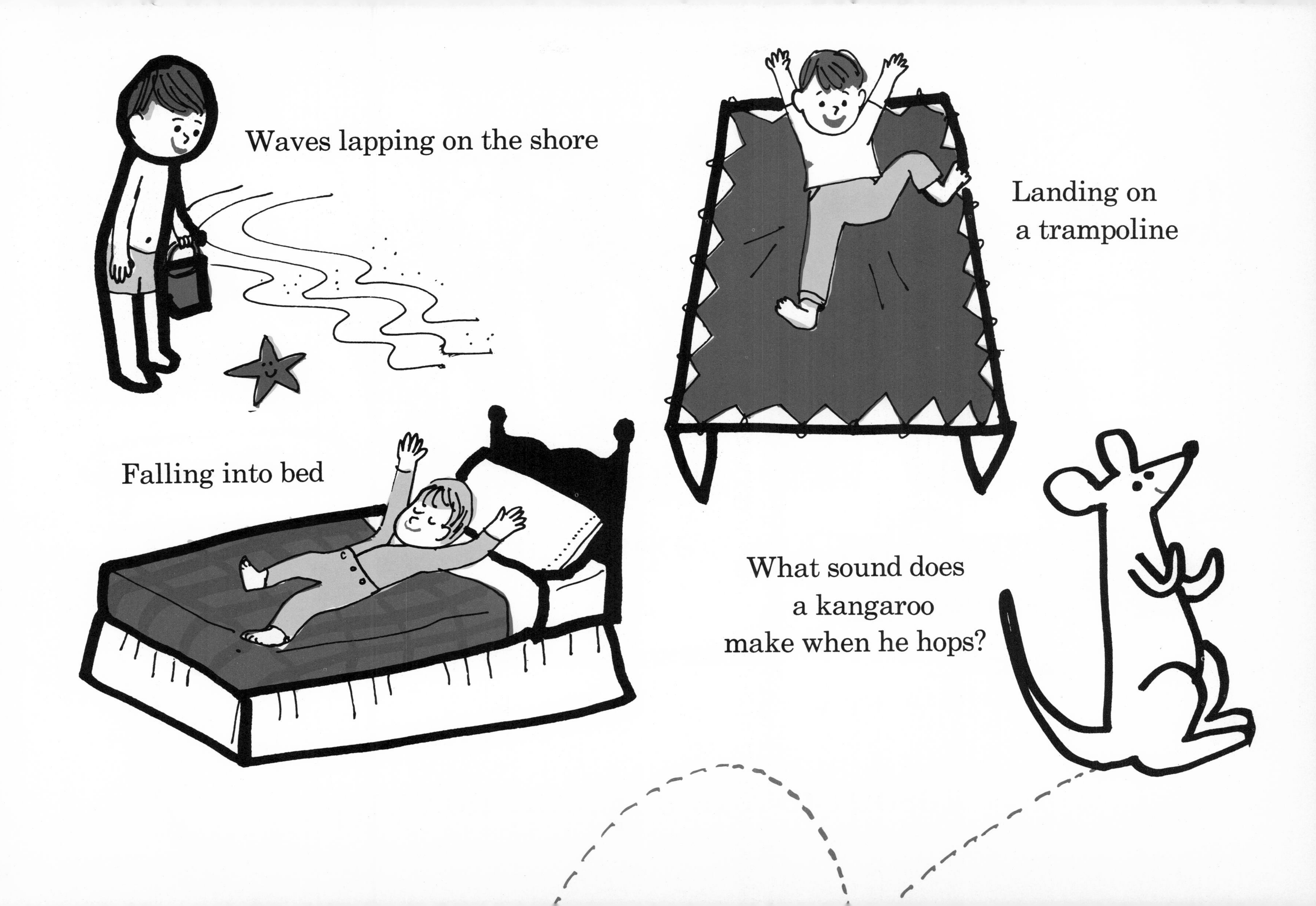
Waves lapping on the shore
Landing on
a trampoline
Falling into bed
What sound does
a kangaroo
make when he hops?

Now let's take a word like

# ZOOM!

ZOOM is a very fast sound!

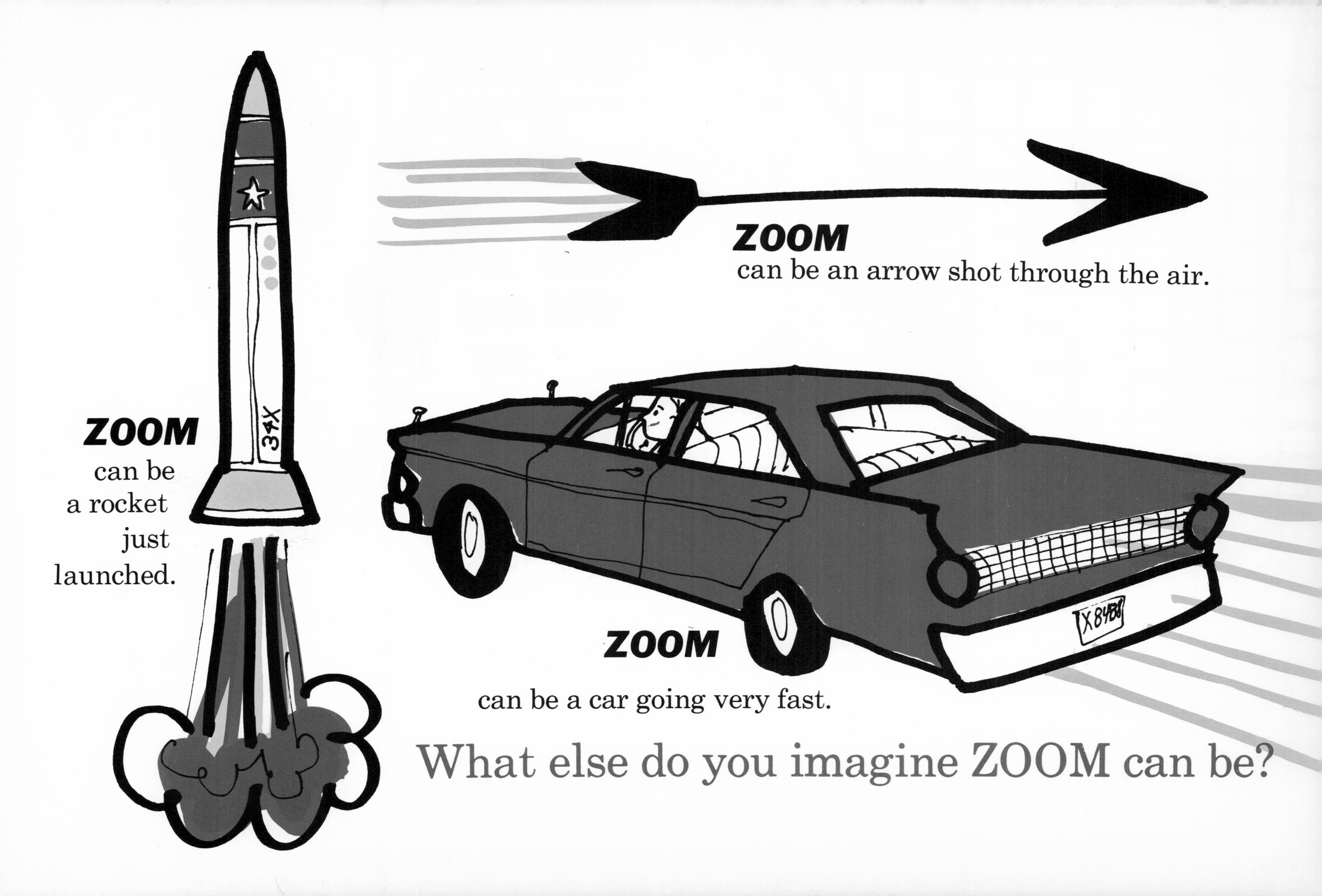
ZOOM
can be an arrow shot through the air.
ZOOM
can be
a rocket
just
launched.
34X
ZOOM
can be a car going very fast.
What else do you imagine ZOOM can be?

# Did you imagine any of these ZOOM sounds?

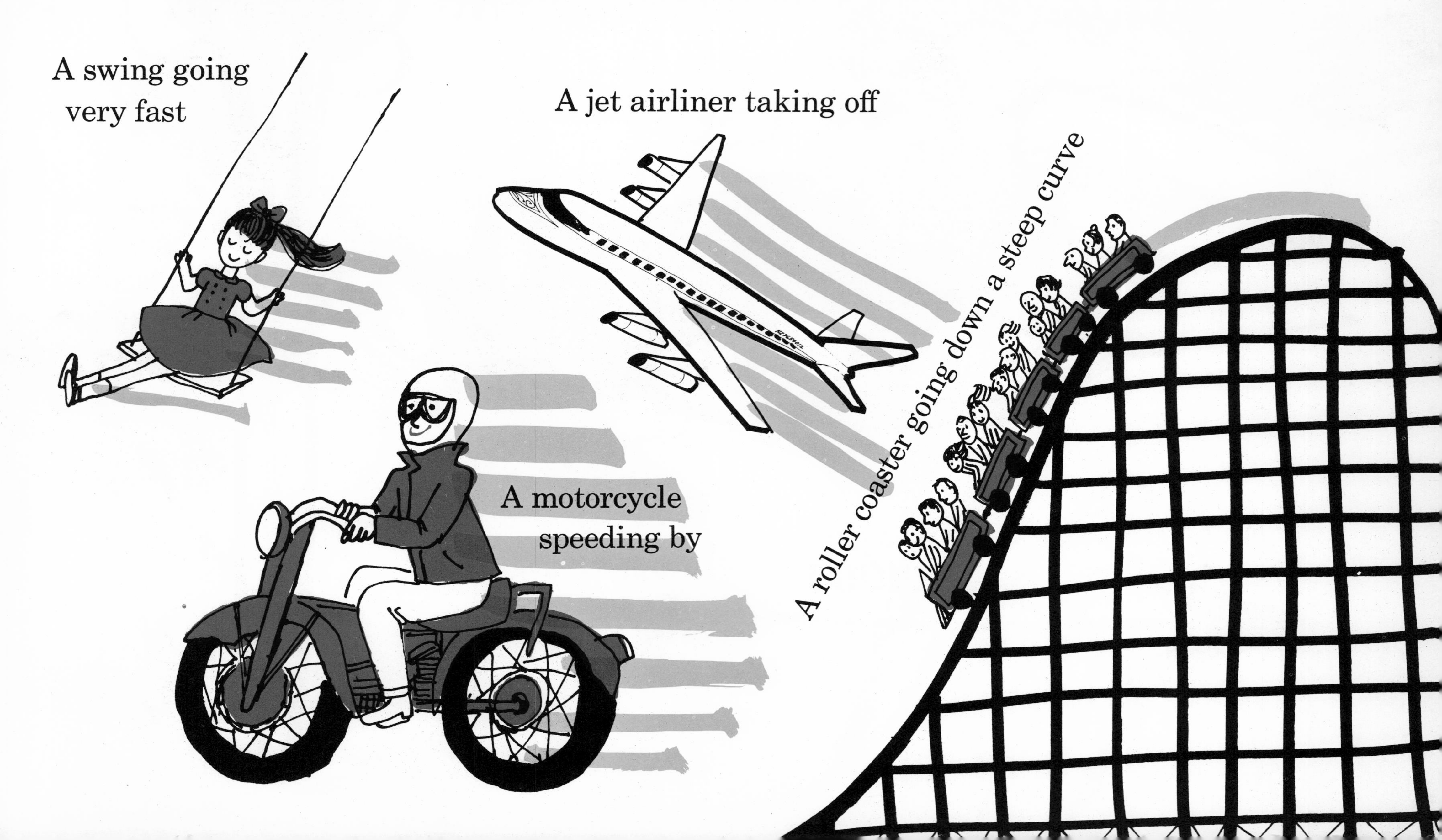

A swing going
very fast

A jet airliner taking off

A motorcycle
speeding by

A roller coaster going down a steep curve

going down a slope

a high fast slide

A seagull diving for a fish

What sound does a porpoise make when he jumps?

Now let's take a word like

BOOM!

BOOM is a very loud sound . . . .

OOM
n be the sound
of a big drum . . .
BOOM
BOOM!
or a car backfiring . . .
BOOM!
BOOM!
BOOM
BOOM
or dynamite exploding !

What else do you imagine BOOM can be?

# Did you imagine any of these things?

A tuba's
oompa-pahs
Thunder over your house
A rug being beaten
A cannon being shot

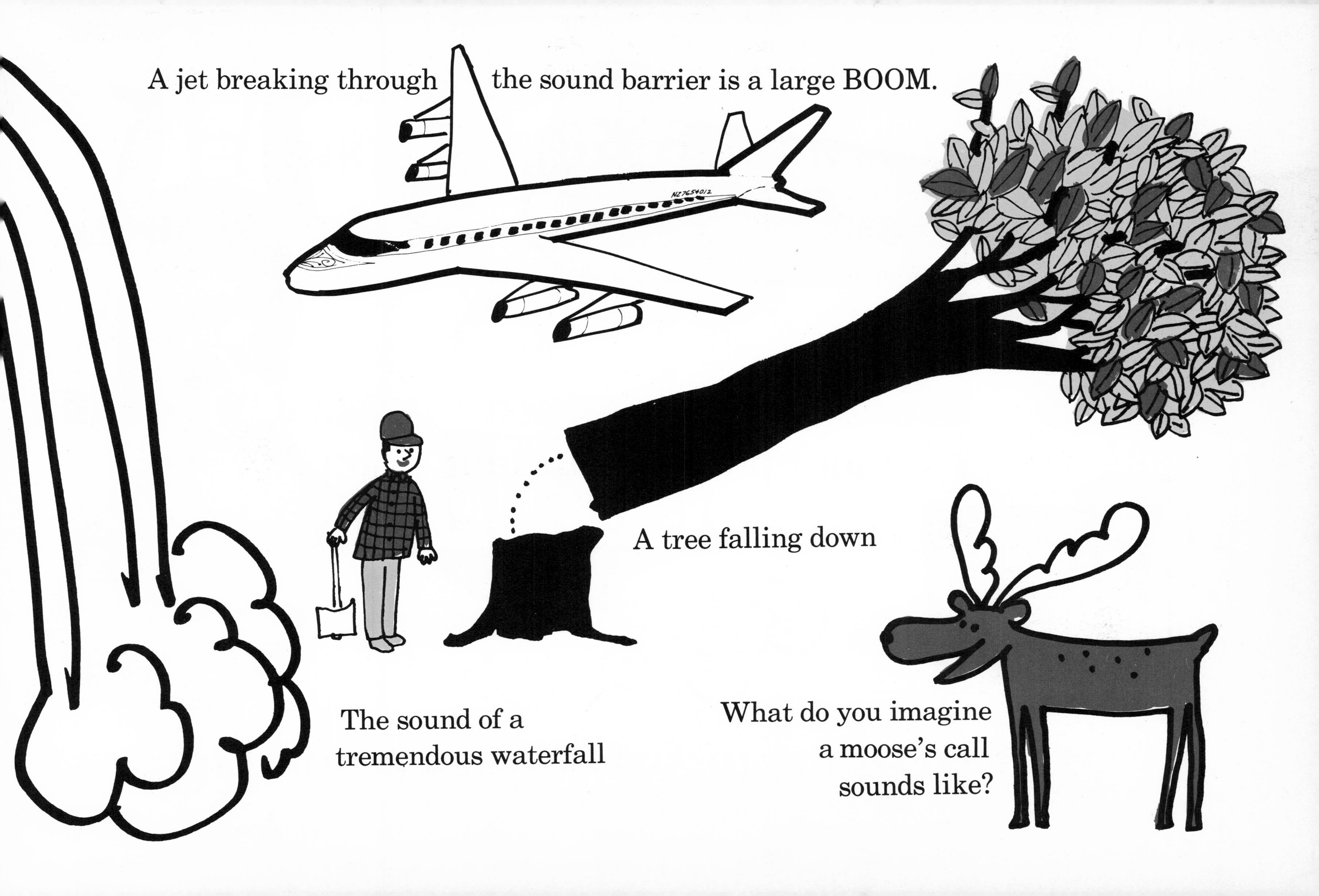
A jet breaking through the sound barrier is a large BOOM.
A tree falling down
The sound of a tremendous waterfall
What do you imagine a moose's call sounds like?

Let’s imagine a sound like . . .

# TINKLE.

Tinkle is a tiny ringing sound.

Coins jingling in a bank are many tinkles.

A pin landing
on a tile floor
is a tinkle.

You hear tinkling
when you
play
jacks.

Can you think of any other tinkling sounds?

# Did you imagine any of these?

High notes on a piano
A charm bracelet jangling
A xylophone being played
A spoon hitting a cup

ree

Beads rattling

A triangle being hit

A small bell

Happy Farms
MILK
MILK

What sound does a milkman delivering milk bottles make?

Are there any other sounds you thought of ?

Now let's imagine a sound like

# CLICK.

CLICK is a quick sound.

A click can be a key turning in a lock . . . .

Each tick of the clock is a click . . . .

An egg cracking is a click.

## What other click sounds can you hear?

# Did you imagine any of these?

Roller skate
wheels turning
are many clicks.
Glasses
hitting
together
Hail on a window
Knife
touching a fork
Turning the knob on a TV set

Someone snapping
a picture

A refrigerator door
being opened or closed

Winding a toy

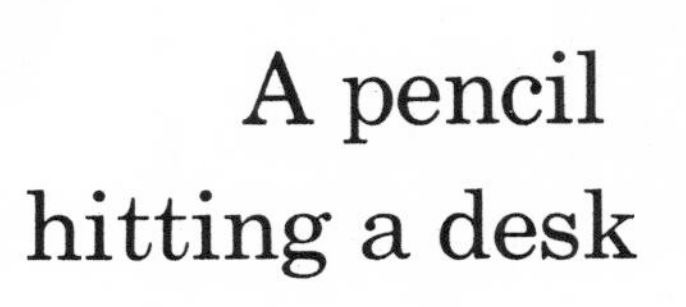

A pencil
hitting a desk

Teeth chattering when you're very cold

Are there any
other sounds you thought of ?

Now let's imagine some other sounds. What sounds do these make?

A mosquito flying
A twig breaking
A zipper closing
A fire burning
Food frying in a pan

SuperWash

Popcorn popping

A bell ringing

A washing machine washing

A baby crying. He just woke up . . . so

NOBODY NEEDS TO

WHISPER ANYMORE. . . .

YOU CAN START TO MAKE NOISE. . .

YIPPEE!

P.S.
YIPPEE is a cowboy sound.